COLOURING BOOK
GUSTAV KLIMT
THE FOUNDER OF
THE VIENNA SECESSION

Contents

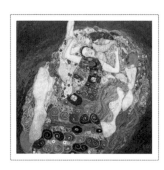

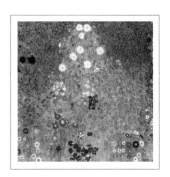

Garden path with chickens
p. 51

Judith I (Judith and Holofernes)
p. 55

Portrait of Fritza Riedler
p. 59

Adele Bloch-Bauer II
p. 63

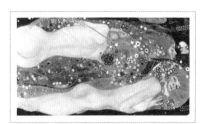

The Water Serpents II
p. 67

Mermaids (Silver Fish)
p. 71

The Kiss
p. 75

Judith II (Salomé)
p. 79

Church in Cassone
p. 83

Hope II
p. 87

Portrait of Johanna Staude
p. 91

Colouring pencils at the ready!

Originally known as "painting books", colouring books first came into being in the 18th century, the brainchild of various painters and educationists who felt the need to promote the practice of art among young people. This enjoyable pastime, recognized as improving the cognitive ability of those who engage in it, went hand in hand with the arrival of colouring pencils, and became popular at the end of the 19th century with the appearance of the first colouring books. These were originally marketed by New York publishers McLoughlin in 1879 and became commonly used by children in the early 1930s. Colouring is an activity accessible to all, both male and female. It is a fascinating and relaxing pastime that helps to promote good motor skills and to develop concentration. Just one key quality is needed: patience. If this is something you lack at times, engaging in this very calming activity is bound to be of benefit. Whether or not you choose to follow the advice we give you here is up to you. The important thing is to let one single objective guide the way you colour: unbridled enjoyment.

Getting started

To feel relaxed when colouring, it's a good idea to create your own space. Gather together everything you need so that you can enjoy your colouring without interruption.

USING PAINTS

BRUSHES

Arm yourself with a selection of brushes of different shapes and thicknesses. Go for quality: nothing is more annoying that a brush that loses its bristles!

PAINTS

Gouache is a very easy medium to use. Soluble and washable in water, it gives bright, intense tones, even when heavily diluted. The colours also blend easily.

In principle, you only really need red, blue, and yellow. With these primary colours, plus a tube of white and one of black, you can create all other colours.

It's up to you to decide how much time you want to spend mixing them!

APPLICATION

Mix your colours on a palette. Make enough to cover all the areas you'll want to paint as it can be difficult to mix exactly the same tone again. Depending on the intensity you want, add more or less water.

Don't overload your brush with paint, and keep a light hand. If the colour isn't intense enough, go back over it, keeping a light touch. You'll soon find out how to adapt what you do to obtain the desired result. And there's nothing to stop you varying thicknesses within the same area.

USING PENCILS

COLOURING PENCILS

When choosing colouring pencils, go for "artist quality" rather than children's pencils. Good quality pencils are softer and less dry, making it easier to blend the colours and achieve more sustained or subtle tones. Before buying an entire set, try different pencils out; this will help you decide which brand you prefer. Keep them in a small plastic container within easy reach, but make sure it's stored in a safe place to prevent the pencils from breaking.

SHARPENERS

If possible, choose a mechanical sharpener that lets you sharpen pencils of different sizes and protects the coloured lead. Failing this, go for a good quality, manual, metal sharpener which can also be useful for sharpening very short pencils. Don't press too hard when you sharpen, as you could break the lead.

ERASERS

Make sure you have vinyl erasers in different sizes so that, if necessary, you can erase very small details or small areas of colour. You can also use them to lighten colours. But be careful not to press too hard or you may damage the paper.

APPLICATION

Begin by checking that your pencils are finely sharpened: this will ensure they give the best, most even results.

You can apply colour in several layers until you obtain the colour density you want. Try one or two very light layers, then gradually increase the pressure, which should remain constant throughout the layer.

If you want to blend colours, alternate the layers. Starting with one or two common background layers, apply different colours to different areas to create a range of shades – if you want to add tone to the sky, for example.

By applying colour in small, overlapping circles, you'll avoid hard lines that can be difficult to soften. Try to work consistently, keeping the same movement and the same pressure.

DON'T FORGET

- A good, stable water pot for cleaning your brushes and diluting your paint. Change the water frequently.
- A rag to wipe your brushes or pencil leads after sharpening ... and your fingers!
- A ruler, which is useful as a guide.
- Paper tissues to absorb any surplus paint and soften pencil lines.

Gustav Klimt

It was in late nineteenth-century Vienna, the capital of a declining Austro-Hungarian Empire and the centre of a teeming and innovative cultural life, that the work of Gustav Klimt was produced. Though it is now celebrated, in his lifetime it was considered scandalous; it was denigrated, ridiculed, and despised by the Austrian establishment. Yet the talent and brilliance of this artist, who became the leading figure in the Vienna Secession – a trend that aspired to completely regenerate art in a fin-de-siècle period still hesitating between academicism and modernity – paved the way for Art Nouveau and, beyond that, for modern painting. The gold and decorative patterns so characteristic of Klimt remain a symbol of this artistic revolution.

Classical training in Vienna

Gustav Klimt was born on 14 July 1862 in Baumgarten, a suburb of Vienna. He was the second in a family of seven children. His father, Ernest Klimt, was a gold engraver and his mother, Anna Finster, was an opera singer. Early on, Gustav developed a taste for art and demonstrated excellent drawing skills. In 1876, when he was just 14 years old, Gustav won a scholarship to the Vienna School of Arts and Crafts, where he received classical training. He followed Professor Laufberger's painting classes, and specialized in architectural painting. He was curious about a wide variety of techniques, and explored mosaic and fresco painting. His ambition at that time was to become an art teacher; but his gifts would very soon open up broader prospects. While still a student, he received several commissions and began painting portraits from photos so as to supplement his income. Then, in 1879, Klimt joined the team of the famous painter Hans Makart, whom he thought of as a role model.

An official painter recognized by all

In 1883, after his graduation, Klimt founded a studio with his brother Ernst and a mutual friend, Franz Matsch: they called it the "Company of Viennese artists". The trio decided to specialize in murals, abandoning personal work for the time being. The skill and finesse of their work were soon recognized and their studio was asked to decorate the walls and ceilings of houses, as well as theatres and public buildings. The three artists produced a great deal of work in common (frescoes and allegories), in a very academic neoclassical style. For example, they decorated the assembly hall of the Sturany Palace in Vienna, the Hermes Villa in the Lainzer Tiergarten in 1885, the Carlsbad theatre in 1886, and the stairs of the Vienna Burgtheater in 1888: that year, Gustav Klimt received the Golden Order of Merit for art from Emperor Franz Josef. But the main event that would ensure the group's reputation as painters was the completion of the decoration of the grand staircase of the Kunsthistorisches Museum in 1890-1891. It was at this time that the Klimt brothers and Franz Matsch joined the Vienna Artists' Association, a conservative group that controlled artists' exhibitions in the capital.

Breaking away

At 27, Gustav Klimt was a recognized, official, and totally "conventional" painter who had enjoyed both esteem and success. By 1890, however, he had begun to try and break away from Viennese academicism. Two personal events would impact on his destiny as a painter. In 1891, his brother Ernst married Helene Flöge. The same year, Gustav painted the portrait of her young sister Emilie. This meeting marked the beginning of an unwavering romantic friendship, and had a fundamental impact on the direction Klimt's painting took thereafter. But it was undeniably the successive deaths of his father and Ernst in 1892 that had the profoundest effect on his life. Deeply affected by this double bereavement, Klimt began to question and ultimately reject the academicism which he had always forced himself to follow, and sought to develop a more personal kind of painting.

In 1894 the studio, which had been floundering since the death of Ernst, was given the commission for a vast fresco intended to decorate the ceiling of the Great Hall of the University of Vienna. In the years from 1894 to 1897, Klimt pursued his personal quest. He joined the circle of Emilie Flöge, who had created a fashion house, and also became friends with the writers Arthur Schnitzler, Hugo von Hofmannsthal, and Hermann Bahr. He also took an interest in French symbolism and Impressionism. Vienna was then a bustling capital with a vibrant cultural life. Freud, Mahler, Wittgenstein, and Schnitzler personified the emerging capacity for innovation shown by the elite of Vienna as they rebelled against the cautious conformism of Franz Josef's Austria. The art of Klimt and his friends was not as revolutionary as the art being produced in France at that time, but their work nonetheless laid bare the crisis then afflicting European society.

In 1895, at an exhibition in the Austrian capital, Klimt discovered the works of Max Liebermann, Félicien Rops, Max Klinger, Arnold Böcklin, and Rodin. Klimt, who wanted to break free of what he felt were academic depictions, found in symbolism a new form of expression, and gradually moved away from representational painting.

The Vienna Secession

In April 1897, Klimt and fifteen or so other painters, including Koloman Moser, Josef Olbrich, Rudolf Bacher and Carl Moll, resigned from the Vienna Artists' Association and founded a group called the "Vienna Secession", which sought to overhaul the artistic life of the era and create a new building dedicated to the arts. Klimt very quickly became the president of the "Secessionists", who aimed to break free of Viennese conservatism which, in their view, was responsible for total "obscurantism". They endeavoured to produce works which would "win international recognition for Austrian art" and bridge the gap between Art with a capital A and the so-called minor arts, by making utilitarian objects more like works of art. The Secession was in some respects a Viennese variation of the vast European trend (Art Nouveau in France, Jugendstil in Germany) which, for more than twenty years, had brought beauty into the cityscape and into everyday life through new techniques that extended to architecture and the decorative arts.

In 1898, less than a year after its birth, the Secession had its own forum, the journal *Ver Sacrum (Sacred Spring)* and its flagship building, the pavilion built by Josef Olbrich to fulfil Klimt's wish that young figurative artists could have a permanent place to exhibit their works. The Secession could now proclaim its motto loud and clear: "To every age its art. To every art its freedom."

As the year of the new departure, 1897 marked the beginning of a very productive artistic period for Klimt. Now feeling liberated, he painted many pictures and produced nearly four thousand drawings. He abandoned the illusionistic rendering of space, with its perspective effects and *trompe l'oeil*, in favour of a two-dimensional surface where lines, colours, and rhythms were organized amidst an ornamental profusion. His favourite themes at this time were eroticism, the depiction of the fragility of the body and the transience of love. Despite the support of an enlightened and sensitive business class, his new paintings aroused the indignation of the conservative bourgeoisie of Vienna, who were soon denouncing his work as shocking.

The first scandals

The first Secession exhibition was held the following year, in the pavilion of the same name. It was very popular, attracting a large audience. Among the key works of this first show was a painting by Klimt entitled Pallas Athena, which triggered an outcry – the first of many. The painter ironically subverted the traditional representation of the goddess by showing her in the guise of a femme fatale, with a gorgon sticking her tongue out on her breastplate. There were howls of protest at this irreverent depiction.

History repeated itself just two years later, when in 1900, on the occasion of the seventh Secession exhibition, Klimt presented a painting entitled Philosophy. This was the first of three preparatory paintings for the mural commissioned six years earlier by the University of Vienna, together with Medicine and Jurisprudence. In this fresco (destroyed by the Nazis in 1945), Klimt chose to represent Philosophy as a sphinx with a blurred outline, her head lost amid the stars, surrounded by the cycles of life, from birth to old age, via the embraces of love. In the foreground, Knowledge assumes the guise of a femme fatale fixing her cold, dark eyes upon the viewer. The university authorities, who were expecting a more traditional representation of the subject, thought that this allegory promoted licentiousness and constituted an assault on public decency. The press accused Klimt of insulting education and seeking to pervert the young people of the day. He was accused of creating over-erotic paintings, and questions were even raised about his mental health. The other two frescoes, Medicine and Jurisprudence, presented some time later, were met with equal indignation. A petition was circulated, asking that they not be installed in the Aula Magna (the Great Hall). The scandal was such that in 1905 the artist decided not to fulfil his commission and bought the three heavily-criticized panels back from the Ministry. In 1902, Klimt was still persevering. At the fourteenth Secession exhibition, devoted to the music of Beethoven, he presented the Beethoven Frieze, a fresco in seven panels illustrating the Ninth Symphony, meant to decorate a monument in memory of the composer by the architect Josef Hoffmann. In Hoffmann's view, the memorial should be a total art work involving painting, music and architecture. The frieze was severely criticized from a moralistic standpoint, but it won plaudits for the artist from Rodin and Mahler, for whom "it represents the aspiration to happiness of suffering humanity, which seeks solace in the arts".

The "Golden Cycle" and the end of the Secession

The years 1902-1903 constituted a second turning point in Klimt's work, and a period of intense creativity. This was the beginning of his "Golden Cycle" or "golden period", a very productive time which was to last until 1909. Despite the scathing attacks aroused by his paintings, Klimt's work again met with great success, especially in Paris where his *Medicine* was awarded a gold medal at the Universal Exhibition of 1900. His painting took on a whole new direction. The artist went for a symbolic mode of expression, adopting the decorative richness of Art Nouveau and the influence of Eastern arts, including those of Byzantium and Japan. This period was called "golden" in reference to the quantity of gold leaf he used for the decorative background of his paintings.

From 1904 onwards, Klimt produced several mosaic murals to decorate the dining room of the luxurious palace of the Belgian banker Adolphe Stoclet, built in Brussels to plans laid by Hoffmann. Klimt drew the cartoons for the mosaics, which were executed by the Wiener Werkstätte. The artist's decorative richness came to dramatic fruition in *Expectation* and *Fulfilment*, the first two panels that he delivered to Stoclet. In 1906 he finally painted the third, *The Kiss*, one of his most famous paintings, considered to be the peak of his "Golden Cycle".

Klimt now felt that the Secession had become ossified and in 1905 he decided to withdraw from it, with several friends including Moll. He founded a new group, while Hoffmann and Moser created the Wiener Werkstätte (Vienna Workshops). Klimt now focused on allegorical painting without relief or perspective, often asymmetrical in composition, increasingly stylized and richly ornamented.

He painted landscapes, but mainly women: though he had decided never to marry, Klimt lived among women – his mother and sisters at home, his models, and his wealthy female clients whose portraits he painted in his studio. This bachelor who had so many conquests among women (he had fourteen illegitimate children!) himself admitted: "What subjects for painting interest me? Other people, especially women..." Hence his paintings venerating the figure of woman (*Judith*, 1901; *The Kiss*, 1907-1908); the commissioned portraits (*Fritza Riedler*, 1906; *Adele Bloch-Bauer*, 1907); the scenes depicting women naked or in languorous and erotic poses, always inserted into compositions with a rich, shimmering, all-pervasive, and sensual ornamentation, drawing for its motifs on many different traditions.

The final years

After 1910, the stylization in Klimt's work softened. Some of his great full-length portraits even returned to a rigorous symmetry, conferring a hieratic attitude upon the characters, while the colour was applied in increasingly subtle touches of an almost impressionist facture (*Adele Bloch-Bauer II*, 1912). He refined his style and stopped using gold. The works of the last period sometimes reflected a tendency to tragedy (*Mother with Two Children*, circa 1900-1910), heralding a new era, that of the expressionism of Egon Schiele and Oskar Kokoschka, whose art was directly related to Klimt's.

In 1909, the artist went to Paris where he discovered Toulouse-Lautrec. He had already been to an exhibition at the Vienna Kunstschau where he had encountered Fauvism, Van

Gogh, Munch, Toorop, Gauguin, Bonnard, and Matisse. The following year, he took part in the Venice Biennale that brought him new acclaim. In 1911, *Death and Life* won first prize at the International Exhibition in Rome. Klimt travelled for a few years, to Florence, Rome, Brussels, London, and Madrid. His mother, with whom he had lived all his life, died in 1915. The artist's palette then darkened, sometimes even tending to monochrome. He participated in the exhibition of the Bund Österreichischer Künstler at the Berlin Secession, alongside Schiele and Kokoschka, among others. Klimt was again a recognized painter. In 1917, the Academy of Fine Arts of Vienna and its sister academy in Munich named him an honorary member. He began work on *The Bride* and then on *Adam and Eve*.

Gustav Klimt died in Vienna on 6 February 1918 (or in January, according to some witnesses), probably of a stroke (or, say others, pneumonia), leaving behind many unfinished canvases. His work pits figuration against abstraction, allegory against landscape, stylization against naturalism, hedonism against scepticism, and impressionism against symbolism: this gives it a very special place in art history. Klimt, a persevering precursor, aware that "if you cannot by your actions and art please everyone, then please the few", managed to pave the way for other artistic expressions that proved just as fertile as his own.

Mäda Primavesi

1912, oil on canvas
150 × 110 cm

When Klimt painted the portrait of Mäda Primavesi, the daughter of a banker from Vienna, the child was 9 years old. Long sittings took place in the Viennese painter's studio. Klimt made numerous sketches before deciding on the final composition of this painting. The child, who occupies the full height of the painting, is standing, legs apart, in a self-confident attitude that reflects her determined character. She is wearing a white silk dress decorated with flowers whose colours match those of the room, which is more like a garden than an interior. This is the only child portrait ever painted by the artist, and the first commission from the Primavesi family: Klimt would portray the mother of the family, the actress Eugenia Primavesi, in 1913.

Mäda Primavesi, 1912

Mäda Primavesi, 1912

The Virgin

1913, oil on canvas
200 × 190 cm

Gustav Klimt, a tireless explorer of female sexuality, often painted women's bodies, whether in his portraits, his erotic drawings (of which there are over 4,000) or his frescoes. *The Virgin*, sometimes called *The Maiden*, produced in 1913, deals with a subject dear to the artist: the transformation of the virgin into a woman, or the loss of virginity. The painting is almost square in format, as is typical of Art Nouveau, and represents six women coiled in a spiral evoking the corolla of a flower. The central character seems to be asleep, while parts of her body emerge from the loose, highly decorated garments that envelop her. For some, the central sleeping figure, fully clothed, symbolizes the maiden, while the other characters have faces and poses that express different states of pleasure.

Another interpretation is possible: Klimt's talent lies in showing, under the mass of ornaments, what a prudish Vienna refuses to see. Thus, on closer inspection, prhaps the two bodies in the lower part of the painting, one on the left and one on the right, may represent the spread legs of the girl, and the blue dress in the middle a phallus? The extreme twisting in her neck, anatomically impossible, is a feature found in several of Klimt's works such as *The Kiss* and *The Bride*: it expresses ecstasy. The Viennese painter combines the line and the circle, masculine and feminine, painting and decorating, the conscious and the unconscious.

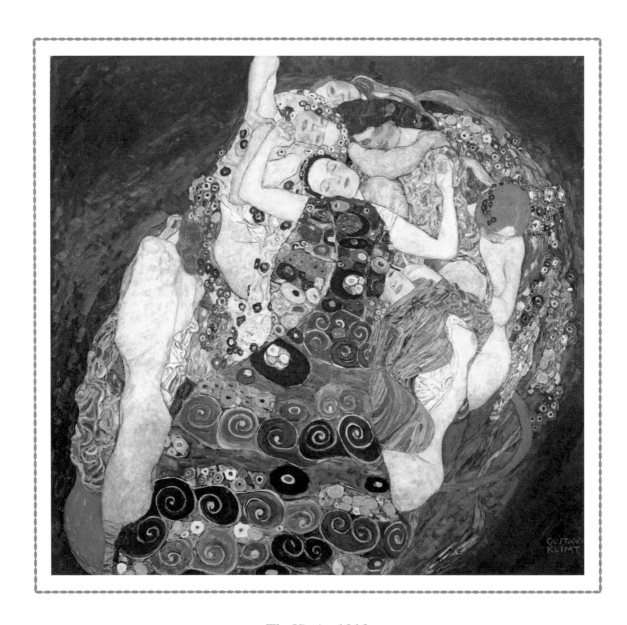

The Virgin, 1913

The Virgin, 1913

The Water Serpents I

1904-1907, oil and gold on parchment
50 × 20 cm

Gustav Klimt was the first painter, before Egon Schiele, to represent the taboo topics of pregnancy, masturbation and lesbianism. *The Water Serpents I*, produced early in his "golden period", is one of several works by Klimt devoted to female couples. To depict female sensuality, the artist here uses the theme of mermaids, a highly popular theme in nineteenth-century art, literature and opera in the German-speaking world. The embrace of its unambiguously lesbian models, unacceptable at the time, would have been censored if the artist had not presented them as allegories, adding a fish-like snake to the background (giving its name to the work) and covering the whole with rich gold- leaf decoration. In 1918, Klimt tackled female homosexuality much more directly in *The Girl-friends* (see p. 47).

The Water Serpents I, 1904-1907

The Water Serpents I, 1904-1907

Portrait of
Adele Bloch-Bauer

1907, oil, gold, and silver on canvas
138 × 138 cm

In 1904, at the request of Ferdinand Bloch-Bauer, who made his fortune in the sugar industry and was the patron of many Secession artists, Klimt began work on the portrait of his wife Adele, which he completed in 1907, the year of his exhibition. It took three years for the artist to finish this work, inspired by the mosaics of the Basilica of San Vitale in Ravenna, particularly those representing the Empress Theodora (sixth century). Forming a square of 138 x 138 centimetres, it is painted on canvas in oil, gold, and silver. Klimt makes innovative and abundant use of gold instead of colour and, five years after the portrait of Emilie Flöge (see p. 35), again follows the principle of large decorative surfaces with only the model's face and hands standing out. The fineness of detail lavished on her face and hands prevents the subject from disappearing into the richness of the complex, refined decoration. *Portrait of Adele Bloch-Bauer* marks a major step in Klimt's portraiture. Looted by the Nazi regime, the painting remained in the Belvedere Museum in Vienna until 2006. After a long legal battle, it was returned to Maria Altmann, the model's niece, and is now exhibited at the Neue Galerie in New York.

Portrait of Adele Bloch-Bauer, 1907

Portrait of Adele Bloch-Bauer, 1907

Portrait of Friederike Maria Beer

1916, oil on canvas
168 × 130 cm

In 1916, Klimt painted the portrait of Friederike Maria Beer, a young woman of Viennese high society, at her request. She had pre-arranged everything: the silk dress with hand-painted Art Nouveau motifs that she called "my Klimt dress", and the little fur-collar coat she bought at the Wiener Werkstätte, the famous Viennese workshops that sprang from the Secession and where she habitually shopped. Inspired by the coat's patterns, Klimt borrowed the details in the background from a Korean vase in his possession: battle scenes, most likely in reference to the First World War. Inspired by oriental art with its horror of empty space, he deliberately overloaded the background, removing any depth in the canvas and melding the subject into the setting. But, as always in Klimt's portraits, the hands and face – whose passivity contrasts here with the sullen expressions of the soldiers – stand out clearly from the whole composition.

Portrait of Friederike Maria Beer, 1916

Portrait of Friederike Maria Beer, 1916

Portrait of Emilie Flöge

1902, oil on canvas
181 × 84 cm

This great portrait of Emilie Flöge, painted in 1902, marks the beginning of a new phase in Klimt's art, characterized by the use of large surfaces covered with decorative motifs in which only the faces and hands of the characters stand out. Klimt did not as yet dare go this far in the portraits executed for his wealthy clients, but the portrait of Emilie Flöge was painted for pleasure, as a tribute to the woman who was his companion for over twenty-five years. They never married and, although Klimt had many love affairs, it is likely that he and Emilie were never lovers. Twelve years his junior, the young woman was distinguished by her spirit of independence, and an entrepreneurial capacity that led to her founding a thriving fashion house in Vienna for which Klimt created many sumptuous fabrics. Sensitive to the feminist ideas in vogue throughout Europe, she joined in the fight against the corset, and tried to impose the fashion of the "reformed dress", a rather shapeless bag-dress – as in this painting – for which Klimt drew several models. The painter produced only two portraits of her: one in 1891, when they met, and this painting from 1902.

Portrait of Emilie Flöge, 1902

Portrait of Emilie Flöge, 1902

Flower garden

1905-1907, oil on canvas

110 × 110 cm

Nearly a quarter of Klimt's pictorial work consists of landscapes, mostly painted around 1900. They were most often produced for the artist's own pleasure during the summer holidays he spent in the Kammer and Attersee region, 250 kilometres from Vienna, when the heat in the capital became unbearable. Painted "from life", these paintings were usually completed in the studio. Unlike the Impressionists, who sought to render the variations of light falling on landscape, Klimt was not interested in atmospheric changes. He preferred to draw inspiration from the painterly solutions of the Neo-Impressionists, applying touches of contrasting colours and short brush strokes. Klimt used a square format (like many Secession artists) to circumscribe the visual field and eliminate the middle ground as well as abolishing distance and perspective. Devoid of any human presence, the painting depicts a timeless state, like a still life whose purpose is both decorative and contemplative. Klimt's landscapes reflect a growing abstraction: what the painter observes is here merely a catalyst. The real subject of the painting is the pictorial structure.

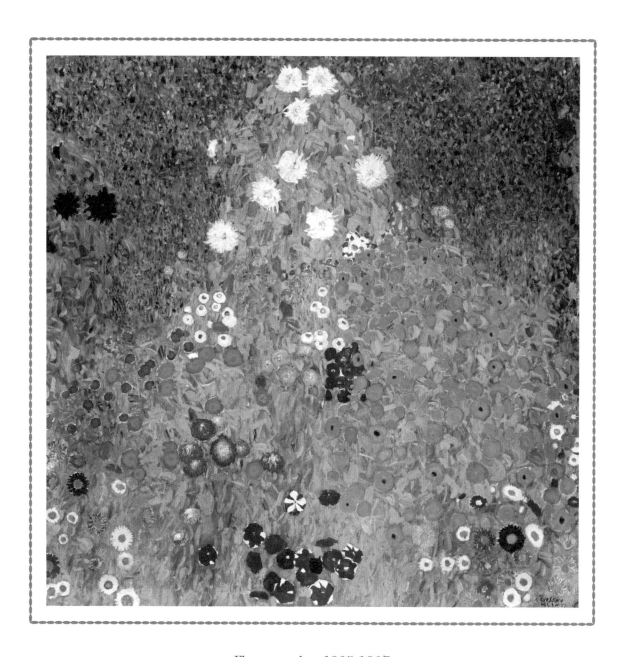

Flower garden, 1905-1907

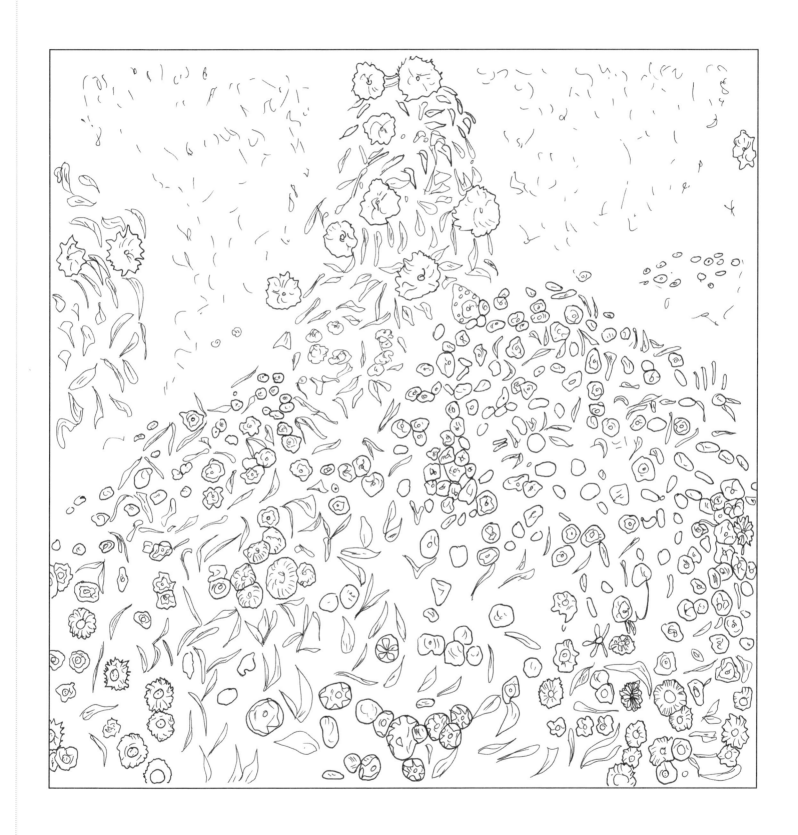

Flower garden, 1905-1907

Fulfilment

1910, mixed media on paper
195 × 120 cm

From 1905-1910, Klimt devoted himself to the frieze commissioned by the Belgian banker Adolphe Stoclet. It was intended for the dining room of the banker's villa in Brussels, built by the Austrian architect Josef Hoffmann. Klimt designed the frieze in the form of a mosaic divided into three phases: in its central part, it represents the *Tree of Life* which, by bringing together all the opposed aspects of the dual world, becomes the symbol of the "unified state"; on the left side, Klimt depicts a young woman dancing, which he called *Expectation*, while on the right he takes up the theme of *The Kiss*, painted in 1907, in a more linear composition, *Fulfilment*. The man leans over the woman as she gives herself to him. The bodies disappear and merge in the abstract ornamental shapes of the clothes that envelop them. The circular designs of the man's clothing evoke the sky and the rectangular shapes of the woman's attire allude to the earth. Thus entwined, this couple symbolizes the fulfilment of a return to the unified state.

Klimt produced nine preparatory sketches for the mural: these have been restored and can again be seen again in the *Museum für Angewandte Kunst* in Vienna. The fresco from the Stoclet Palace, a veritable jewel of Art Nouveau, brings the artist's "Golden Cycle" to a close.

Fulfilment, 1910

Fulfilment, 1910

The Girl-friends

1916-1917, oil on canvas
99 × 99 cm

This canvas, painted in the last years of Klimt's life, once again tackles female homosexuality, but in a gentler and yet more direct way. Here, the painter does not take refuge behind an ornamental or mythological screen. No more sirens or snakes. The artist tenderly represents a couple of women visibly bound together by Sapphic love. It exudes an impression of sweet intimacy, further accentuated by the warm hues and the patterns of flowers and fantastic birds, borrowed from oriental art, that adorn the background. The long neck and the turbaned head of the figure dressed in red add a touch of classical grandeur to the composition. This painting was destroyed in 1945 in the fire at Immendorf Castle.

The Girl-friends, 1916-1917

The Girl-friends, 1916-1917

Garden path with chickens

1916, oil on canvas
110 × 110 cm

This 1917 painting belongs to the group of paintings that the artist produced during his stay in Weissenbach on the shores of Lake Attersee in the summer of 1916. While it has retained the square format dear to Secession painters, the way Klimt so clearly outlines the leaves and flowers suggests that he had by now abandoned his pointillist experiments. This painting was also destroyed in the 1945 fire in Immendorf Castle.

Garden path with chickens, 1916

Garden path with chickens, 1916

Judith I
(Judith and Holofernes)

1901, oil on canvas
84 × 42 cm

In Judith, a character from the Old Testament, Klimt addresses the theme of the castrating woman in all her toxic beauty – already evoked in the Beethoven Frieze of the Secession pavilion. According to the Bible, Judith is a pious and virtuous widow who enters the enemy camp of the Assyrians and captivates their leader Holofernes with her beauty and intelligence, before cutting off his head, thereby contributing to the victory of the Israelites over the Assyrians. This endowed Judith with the status of the heroine who has saved her people. It was not until modern times that she would be considered the symbol of women who use their cunning and seductive ploys to lead men to their doom.

In this painting, Klimt treats Judith as an icon, surrounded by a hammered copper frame that reinforces her sacred character with its decorative profusion. Judith is wearing a transparent tunic that half-shows her right breast, while her left breast and belly are shamelessly displayed, and her voluminous black hair stands out in violent contrast to the gold decor. Judith has just beheaded Holofernes, and her long fingers are caressing her victim's hair, barely noticeable in the lower right corner of the canvas. Yet her face, her half-closed eyes, and her parted lips express ecstatic rapture.

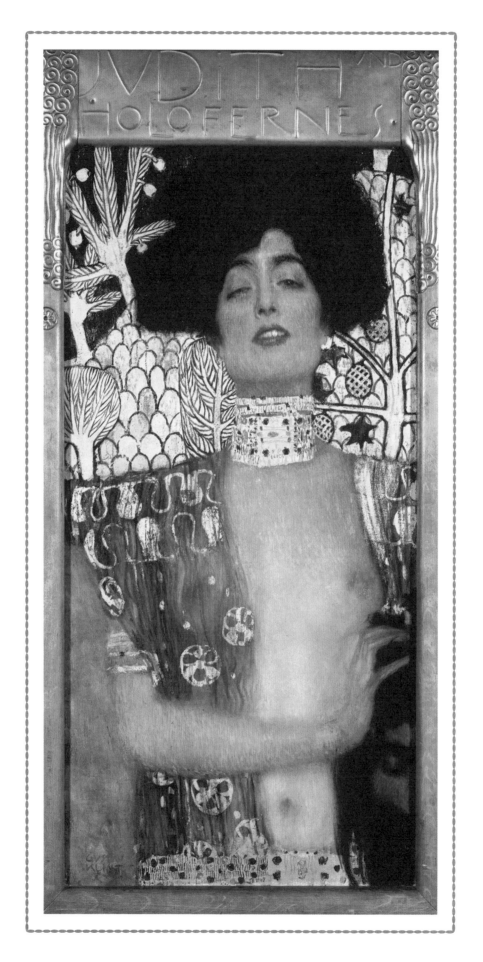

Judith I (Judith and Holofernes), 1901

Judith I (Judith and Holofernes), 1901

Portrait of Fritza Riedler

1906, oil on canvas
152 × 134 cm

In 1906, Klimt, whose portraits were by then very popular among the Viennese elite, painted the wife of the famous Austrian mechanical engineer Alois Riedler. In it we can see the mixture of naturalist and decorative art so characteristic of his paintings. Fritza Riedler is shown in a filmy white dress, sitting on a chair with an indistinct frame and covered with a fabric whose patterns evoke waves. She thus seems to emerge from the bottom of the canvas like a goddess emerging from the waves. The geometric background, consisting of three flat, square, and rectangular areas of colour studded with small gold and silver circles, highlights her face, whose white skin tones echo the colour of her dress. Fritza Riedler wears a semicircular enamel halo headdress reminiscent of those in portraits by Velázquez that the painter must have admired in the museums of Vienna, but also similar to various figures from Ancient Egypt. The care the painter has lavished on the detail of her features hints that this hieratic white woman is no longer in the bloom of youth.

Portrait of Fritza Riedler, 1906

Portrait of Fritza Riedler, 1906

Adele Bloch-Bauer II

1912, oil on canvas
120 × 90 cm

After 1910, Klimt's work began to be less stylized, and some of his full-length portraits returned to a symmetry seen in his earlier years. In 1912, he painted a second portrait of Adele Bloch-Bauer (for the first one, see p. 27), a full-length one this time. The new version has all the features of the artist's late style: he has abandoned gold and silver, but has not lost his love of ornament, nor his desire to flatten space. The colours, now more vivid, are applied in touches of an almost impressionist facture and reflect his study of French painting. The oriental silhouettes in the background are also typical of Klimt's late portraits.

The influence of Japanese prints, visible from the 1890s onwards, is clear – by this point, Klimt's interest in Oriental art had intensified. He bought the complete series of Siegfried Bing's innovative periodical, *Le Japon artistique*, and collected not only Japanese prints, but also Oriental ceramics and silkscreens that he displayed in his studio in Hietzing. Motifs such as the Oriental horse-riders in the background of Adele's portrait were based on the decorations on these ceramics.

Adele Bloch-Bauer II, 1912

Adele Bloch-Bauer II, 1912

The Water Serpents II

1904-1907, oil on canvas
145 × 80 cm

The mermaids glide beneath the water, swimming along in a shoal, brushing past one another in the current that tangles their long flowery hair. They like to rub their bare bellies in the mud. They are also known as "water serpents". They are ambivalent muses that bring together women and water. Klimt played with this mythological image to evoke the female sensuality of which he was a tireless observer. These works were often inspired by scenes of everyday life in his studio where he maintained a tribe of Viennese "working girls", his models, who "twisted and turned" all the time, without really posing; while he drew, he kept a fond eye on them. At the reading of his will, fourteen illegitimate children apparently came forward to make their claims. Klimt, it appears, was not content to be merely a spectator of women!

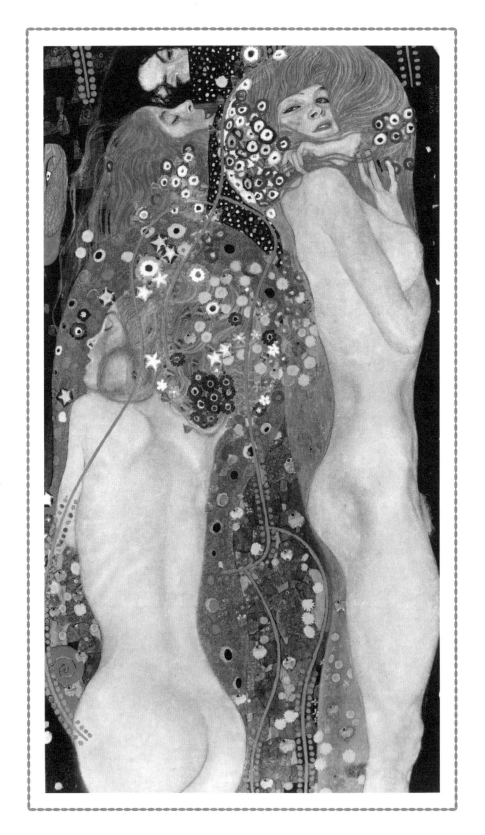

The Water Serpents II, 1904-1907

The Water Serpents II, 1904-1907

Mermaids (Silver fish)

1899, oil on canvas
82 × 52 cm

This painting, produced in 1899, is also known as *Silver Fish*. It is one of the first in which Klimt powerfully combines an erotic image of women with an image of water. Fish seem to have been a masculine symbol for him, sometimes depicted as grotesque or shapeless. As often with Klimt, man is shown more as a voyeur than as an active participant in sexuality. Mermaids, fabulous creatures endowed with a dangerous seductive power, announce the appearance of the theme of the femme fatale in the painter's work.

Mermaids (Silver Fish), 1899

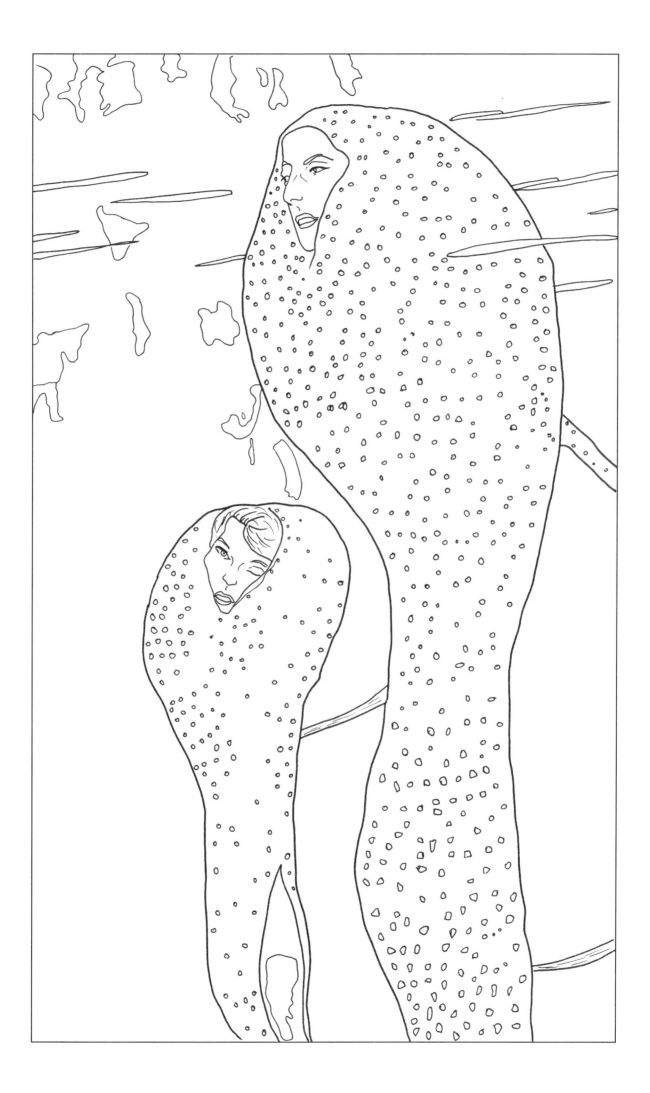

Mermaids (Silver Fish), 1899

The Kiss

1907-1908, oil on canvas
180 × 180 cm

The Kiss is Klimt's most famous work and the painting most emblematic of the artist's "golden period", in which the geometric motifs of ornamentation threatened to swallow up the human element. Here, Klimt succeeded in maintaining the right balance, thanks to his strong, sensual depiction of the characters. Set against a gold background, a kneeling couple, embracing in ecstasy, are set on a carpet of flowers at the edge of a cliff. Their clothes, symbols of bodies merging together, are distinguishable only because of their different patterns: the man's coat is decorated with black and white rectangles that contrast with the round, more brightly coloured motifs on the woman's dress. Only their faces and hands stand out. The powerful embrace of the man and the ecstatic face of the woman give the two lovers, who have become one, an extraordinary presence, forcefully illustrating that divine moment in which passionate love is crystallized.

Klimt used the theme of the kiss several times, in his youth and then when he decorated the dining room of the Stoclet Palace in collaboration with architect Josef Hoffmann. Some have seen this painting to be a "declaration of love," from Klimt to the young Alma Maria Schindler, then aged seventeen and soon to marry Gustav Mahler.

The Kiss, 1907-1908

The Kiss, 1907-1908

Judith II (Salomé)

1909, oil on canvas
178 × 46 cm

In 1909, Gustav Klimt presented a new interpretation of the character of Judith, whom he had already depicted in 1901 (see p. 55), now in a more modern version called *Judith II (Salomé)*. In this life-sized canvas, the artist superimposes the biblical character of Judith onto that of the dancer Salomé. In the centre of the canvas, amidst the twisting and turning curves created by the movement of the dress of Judith-Salomé, what stands out very clearly is the long fingers of the young woman clutching the hair on the head of Holofernes that she has just cut off. This expressive position reflects the evolution of Klimt's painting. While it retains some typical ornamentation, it offers another reading of bodies and faces. Klimt is now endeavouring to highlight the malaise of the soul and the promptings of the flesh. The artist's investigations into nudity, the skin tones of the body, and the appearance and position of the hands all lay the foundations of Expressionism, a movement that developed in the early twentieth century, in the atmosphere of tension and unrest preceding the 1914 war.

Judith II (Salomé), 1909

Judith II (Salomé), 1909

Church in Cassone

1913, oil on canvas

110 × 110 cm

Church in Cassone (Landscape with Cypresses) was painted in the summer of 1913 during Klimt's break of a few weeks on the shores of Lake Garda with Emilie Flöge. Klimt produced three paintings during this stay, one of which has since been destroyed. The artist's holiday resort was located a few kilometres from the village of Cassone, and the painter observed his subject through the lens of a telescope, which perhaps explains the narrow frame. As always for his landscapes, Klimt adopted a square format – a way of flattening the landscape – and built up his canvas around the contrast between the perspective induced by the rooftops and the almost total flatness of the rest of the image. He focused on the glitter of the colours, adding paint in small touches.

Church in Cassone, 1913

Church in Cassone, 1913

Hope II

1907-1908, oil, gold and silver on canvas
110 × 110 cm

After painting transparent, sculptural virgins, and then fallen women and femmes fatales, Klimt began the *Cycle of Life* with its depictions of motherhood. In 1907-1908, he composed *Hope II*, an oil on canvas painting of a young pregnant woman dressed in a long robe decorated with motifs similar to Russian icons (unlike *Hope I*, where she was naked). She stands in profile, which highlights her pregnancy, and bends her head down to look at her belly. We see a skull emerging from her belly and, at her feet, several women who seem to be praying or begging: the picture depicts a death wish, or hope for life. It is as if Klimt, who initially gave this painting the title *Visions*, had reopened a window on life and renounced the darkness that sometimes marked his painting. The background, inspired by Byzantine mosaics, contrasts with the modernity of the subject, influenced by the work of Freud and Viennese psychoanalysis.

Hope II, 1907-1908

Hope II, 1907-1908

Portrait of Johanna Staude

1917, oil on canvas

70 × 50 cm

Portrait of Johanna Staude, left unfinished, is one of the last to be painted by Klimt before his death. For several years, the artist had been refining his style. One is struck by the bare decor, and the simple orange background. This is left empty, in the style of the young expressionist painters of the day, Schiele and Kokoschka, whom Klimt had got to know. Here, all the attention is focused on the model. No staging, nothing "decorative", no symbolism: just a half-length portrait in the manner of a photographic close-up. Only the dress of the young woman is decorated with a blue pattern, obviously unfinished. Klimt, who had long aspired to represent the inner nature of human beings – under the influence of the psychoanalytic thinking developed by Freud – now strips his portraits of the "frills" that had once served to reveal their identity, focusing instead on his subjects' faces and capturing the depth of their gaze.

Portrait of Johanna Staude, 1917

Portrait of Johanna Staude, 1917

Acknowledgements

Mäda Primavesi, 1912, The Metropolitan Museum of Art, New York © The Metropolitan Museum of Art, Dist. RMN-Grand Palais / Schecter Lee • *The Virgin,* 1913, National Gallery, Prague © akg-images • *The Water Serpents I,* 1904-1907, the Belvedere Museum, Vienna © DeAgostini / Leemage • *Portrait of Adele Bloch-Bauer,* 1907, Neue Galerie, New York © Luisa Ricciarini / Leemage • *Portrait of Friederike Maria Beer,* 1916, Tel Aviv Museum of Art, Mizne-Blumental Collection © akg-images / Erich Lessing • *Portrait of Emilie Flöge,* 1902, Museum Karlsplatz, Vienna © Luisa Ricciarini / Leemage • *Flower Garden,* 1905-1907, private coll. © Christie's Images / Bridgeman Images • *Fulfilment,* 1910, Österreichisches Museum für Angewandte Kunst (MAK), Vienna © DeAgostini / Leemage • *The Girl-friends,* 1916-1917 © Photo Austrian Archives / Scala Florence • *Garden path with chickens,* 1916 © akg-images / Erich Lessing • *Judith I (Judith and Holofernes),* 1901, Belvedere Museum, © Vienna Photo Austrian Archives / Scala Florence • *Portrait of Fritza Riedler,* 1906, Belvedere Museum, Vienna © DeAgostini / Leemage • *Adele Bloch-Bauer II,* 1912, Belvedere Museum, Vienna © akg-images / Erich Lessing • *The Water Serpents II,* 1904-1907, private coll. © akg-images / Erich Lessing • *Mermaids (Silver Fish),* 1899, Kunstsammlung Bank Austria Creditanstalt, Vienna © DeAgostini / Leemage • *The Kiss,* 1907-1908, Belvedere Museum, Vienna © Photo Austrian Archives / Scala Florence (interior and cover) • *Judith II (Salome),* 1909, International Gallery of Modern Art, Venice © FineArtImages / Leemage • *Church in Cassone,* 1913, private coll. © akg-images • *Hope II* 1907-1908, The Museum of Modern Art, New York © FineArtImages / Leemage • *Portrait of Johanna Staude,* 1917, Belvedere Museum, Vienna © Luisa Ricciarini / Leemage

An Hachette UK Company
www.hachette.co.uk

Originally published in 2016 by Éditions du Chêne
First published in Great Britain in 2016 by Octopus Books
This edition published in 2016 by Octopus Books, a division of
Octopus Publishing Group Ltd
Carmelite House
50 Victoria Embankment
London EC4Y 0DZ
www.octopusbooks.co.uk

Original title: *Cahier de coloriages Gustav Klimt, le fondateur de la sécession Viennoise*

Copyright © 2016, Éditions du Chêne – Hachette Livre
www.editionsduchene.fr

ISBN 978-0-60063-427-0

A CIP catalogue record for this book is available from the British Library.

Printed and bound in Spain

10 9 8 7 6 5 4 3 2 1

Publishing Director: Denise Bates
Editor: Phoebe Morgan
Production Controller: Sarah Kramer
Translation: Andrew Brown in association with First Edition Translations Ltd, Cambridge, UK
Drawings: Mustapha Oucherif
Introduction text: Dominique Foufelle
Artist biography and references: Isabelle de Couliboeuf
Photoengraving: Quat'Coul